Christopher Hampton was born in the Azores in 1946. He wrote his first play, *When Did You Last See My Mother?*, at the age of eighteen. Since then, his plays have included *The Philanthropist*, *Savages*, *Tales from Hollywood*, *Les Liaisons Dangereuses*, *White Chameleon* and *The Talking Cure*. He has translated plays by Ibsen, Molière, von Horváth, Chekhov and Yasmina Reza (including *Art* and *Life x 3*). His television work includes adaptations of *The History Man* and *Hotel du Lac*. His screenplays include *The Honorary Consul*, *The Good Father*, *Dangerous Liaisons*, *Mary Reilly*, *Total Eclipse*, *The Quiet American*, *Carrington*, *The Secret Agent* and *Imagining Argentina*, the last three of which he also directed.

# CHRISTOPHER HAMPTON

# Embers

based on the novel by
## SÁNDOR MÁRAI

as translated by Carol Brown Janeway

*faber and faber*

First published in 2006
by Faber and Faber Limited
3 Queen Square London WC1N 3AU

Typeset by Country Setting, Kingsdown, Kent CT14 8ES
Printed in England by Mackays of Chatham plc, Chatham, Kent

A CIP record for this book
is available from the British Library

ISBN 0–571–23243–4
978–0–571–23243–7

2 4 6 8 10 9 7 5 3 1

**Embers** was commissioned and produced by Eric Abraham for Portobello Productions in association with Robert Haggiag. The play was first presented at the Duke of York's Theatre, London, on 15 February 2006. The cast was as follows:

**Henrik** Jeremy Irons
**Konrad** Patrick Malahide
**Nini** Jean Boht

*Directed by* Michael Blakemore
*Set designed by* Peter J. Davison
*Lighting designed by* Mark Henderson
*Sound designed by* John Leonard
*Costumes designed by* Sue Willmington

# Characters

**Henrik**
**Konrad**
**Nini**

# EMBERS

# One

*Henrik's room: a large, plain room with a vaulted ceiling; it was once, in fact, two rooms, as its central column suggests, on the first floor of a remote eighteenth-century Hungarian castle. A leather screen partially conceals a monastic bed and enamel washbasin. Large windows look out across parklands towards majestic chestnut trees. Between two of the windows hangs a mid-nineteenth-century Viennese portrait of Henrik's mother, showing an attractive, somehow unmistakably French young woman with a pink straw hat, sensual lips and a plunging décolleté, an incongruously feminine contrast to the masculine severity of the room; while between another two windows, a ghostly greyish rectangle on the dark wallpaper suggests a second painting has at some point been removed. On the wall opposite to the bed and basin is an open wood fireplace, set but not yet lit; around it are disposed three armchairs, one upholstered in French silk, one of the kind known as a 'Florentine chair' and a third which, to judge by how worn and scuffed its brown leather has become, must be Henrik's customary seat. Finally, there's a tall, open wardrobe and, in the opposite corner, a high desk, at which it is necessary to stand in order to write.*

*Henrik is a seventy-five-year-old retired general of the old Kaiserlich-Königlich Austro-Hungarian army, his back still ramrod-straight, his aura formidably distinguished.*

*Dressed impeccably in black, he is over by the desk, holding in one hand his white dress-uniform and in the other a row of medals which he holds up against the chest of the uniform jacket. A low summer sun bathes the room in golden light. It's 14 August 1940, although it will be some time before we become aware of this; our first impression is of some considerably earlier date.*

*Henrik gives a kind of sceptical grunt, puts the medals back on the desk and crosses to the wardrobe, where he hangs up the uniform and closes the door on it. Then he moves back to the desk and stows the medals away in a drawer, his expression thoughtful. He produces a very small key, unlocks a long shallow drawer, opens it, reaches in to release a secret compartment and brings out a compact, useful-looking revolver. He breaks it open, checking that it's loaded, spins the chamber, snaps it shut and lays it on the desk. Then he reaches further into the drawer to find a notebook bound in yellow velvet, also tied with blue ribbon and sealed with wax. For a moment he contemplates the notebook, which has the word* SOUVENIR *stamped on the cover. It's just small enough to fit in his inside pocket, which is where he now stows it. Then he crosses to the window and stands staring out into the twilight.*

*He looks up at a light, almost feathery knock at the door, which immediately opens to reveal Nini. Nini is ninety-one years old, formally dressed in black with a white, starched cap; once Henrik's wet-nurse and nanny, she now runs the domestic affairs of the castle and is always treated by Henrik with the absolute respect due to an equal. He gestures towards the window.*

**Henrik**  So; he's come back.

**Nini**  Yes.

*He turns to her; and she considers him steadily for a moment, with the air of someone who knows everything there is to know about him.*

That first summer he spent here, you were only eleven, you know what your mother said?

4

**Henrik** What?

**Nini** She was watching you both climbing into the carriage on your way back to the Military Academy; and she said to me: 'At last, a happy marriage!'

*Henrik allows himself a brief, rueful smile.*

And I said: 'One day Konrad will leave him and the suffering will be terrible.'

**Henrik** You know everything.

**Nini** And then she said: 'You always lose the person you love: and if you're not able to bear that loss, then you're a failure as a human being.'

*Henrik nods in silent agreement, glancing up at his mother's portrait; then he takes a more businesslike tone.*

**Henrik** What are we planning to serve him?

**Nini** Trout. Trout followed by beef. Then a guinea-fowl. Flambéed ice cream. I'm a little anxious about that. The chef hasn't made it for more than ten years.

**Henrik** Last time we had crayfish.

**Nini** Krisztina always liked crayfish. They didn't have any today.

**Henrik** Bring up some Chablis. And the '86 Pommard for the beef.

**Nini** It's already on the table.

**Henrik** And a magnum of Mumm.

**Nini** We only have the brut. Krisztina drank all the demi-sec.

**Henrik** Really? She didn't like champagne. She never drank more than a mouthful.

**Nini**  All the same . . .

*Henrik indicates the old leather chair.*

**Henrik**  Last time, the day of the hunt, he sat in my chair.

**Nini**  What a memory.

**Henrik**  I sat in the Florentine chair and . . . Krisztina sat in the chair my mother brought from Paris. And there were dahlias on the table. In the blue crystal vase.

**Nini**  You remember every detail.

**Henrik**  I do. Are we having the Sèvres?

**Nini**  Yes.

**Henrik**  And the blue candles on the table?

**Nini**  I hadn't remembered that.

**Henrik**  We do have them, don't we?

**Nini**  Yes, of course.

**Henrik**  Good.

*He looks up at the pale space on the wall: Nini notices at once.*

**Nini**  Do you want the picture hung back up?

**Henrik**  We still have it, do we?

**Nini**  Yes.

*Henrik hesitates for a second; then shakes his head.*

**Henrik**  No.

*Pause.*

I thought you might have burned it.

**Nini**  What's the sense in burning pictures?

**Henrik**  You're quite right.

*Nini moves, as if she's preparing to leave the room: then she turns back to Henrik.*

**Nini**  What is it you want from this man?

**Henrik**  The truth.

**Nini**  But you know the truth.

**Henrik**  I do not! The truth is exactly what I don't know.

**Nini**  You know the facts.

**Henrik**  The facts are only part of the truth. Not even Krisztina knew the truth. Whereas Konrad . . . I'm going to get the truth from him. After forty-one years.

*Silence.*

**Nini**  There's something I never told you. Krisztina: when she was dying, she asked for you.

*Henrik stares at her, motionless.*

You were at the lodge. I was alone with her. And she asked for you. I'm telling you because it's something you ought to know this evening.

*In the ensuing silence comes the sound of an approaching carriage. Henrik moves to look out of the window.*

**Henrik**  Here he is. Have him brought up here.

**Nini**  Yes.

*She moves to the door, then pauses in the doorway and turns back.*

Promise me you won't get upset.

**Henrik**  I promise.

*She leaves the room. The sound of the carriage grows. Henrik takes the revolver off the desk, moves back to the window, standing to one side so as not to be seen in the window, raises the revolver and takes aim.*

*Blackout.*

# Two

*Five minutes later. Konrad stands framed in the doorway for a second, before advancing into the room. He's also seventy-five, slight and pale, though giving no impression of frailty. He's wearing a very well-cut dark suit. Henrik moves across to shake hands with him. The atmosphere is formal. There's no sign of the revolver. Konrad breaks the silence, speaking softly.*

**Konrad**  I came back.

**Henrik**  I knew you would.

*Henrik releases Konrad's hand and stands for a moment scrutinising him intently.*

**Konrad**  You're right: neither of us is getting any younger.

**Henrik**  No: but for some reason we have both endured.

**Konrad**  Yes.

**Henrik**  Absinthe?

**Konrad**  Thank you.

*Henrik moves to a table, where the elements have been prepared: glasses, into which he pours a measure of brownish liquid; silver strainers, on to each of which he places a sugar lump; and a water jug, from which he pours water over the sugar lump into the glass below, where the absinthe turns a vivid jade-green. Over this the conversation proceeds.*

**Konrad**  I'm not sure I remember this room.

**Henrik** No. It used to be two rooms, in fact: my mother's bedroom and dressing room. I had it converted a long time ago. I always liked the view.

*Konrad glances out of the window, towards the setting sun.*

**Konrad** Yes.

**Henrik** I was born in this room.

**Konrad** Really?

**Henrik** And I have every intention of dying in it.

**Konrad** Well: not many people can say that.

**Henrik** No.

*Konrad indicates the leather chair.*

**Konrad** This chair, on the other hand, I do remember.

*He sits in it.*

And these others, unless I'm much mistaken.

*Henrik brings over his drink and hands it to him.*

Not bad after forty-one years.

**Henrik** And forty-three days. Your health.

*He raises his glass and drinks. Konrad follows suit.*

Where have you come from?

**Konrad** London.

**Henrik** Is that where you live now?

**Konrad** Just outside. I bought a small house when I got back from the tropics.

**Henrik** Oh? Whereabouts in the tropics?

**Konrad** Singapore. Before that, up country in the Malay peninsula.

**Henrik** Very ageing, the tropics are said to be.

**Konrad** Yes: they'll knock ten years off your life. They use you up and spit you out. They kill something in you.

**Henrik** Is that why you went?

*Konrad looks at him for a moment, as if surprised that he has gone on to the attack so soon.*

**Konrad** Yes.

**Henrik** And did you succeed? In killing whatever it was?

*Silence.*

**Konrad** The first year you never stop thinking you're going to die. After three years, you realise you're not the same person any more and never will be. Eventually, you've no idea what's going on any more. You lie there, night after night, listening to the rain drumming against the roof: and finally you start to get angry. A lot of people turn either murderous or suicidal.

**Henrik** Not the English, surely?

**Konrad** The English bring England with them in their suitcases: their golf courses; their whisky; their reserve; their polite air of superiority; their dinner-jackets, which they climb into every single night out in the swamps. But even they get infected with this rage, sooner or later. That's why, back in England, anyone who's spent any length of time in the tropics is suspect. However respectable they may be and however carefully they observe the formalities, there's always something too rigid about them, like a drunk who enunciates too carefully. They can't conceal the chaos inside.

**Henrik** And is there chaos inside you?

*Konrad looks at him for a moment, frowning.*

Isn't that what you came here to tell me?

*Silence. Eventually, Konrad shakes his head.*

**Konrad** No. I came here because I was in the vicinity. In Vienna. I came because I wanted to see you one last time.

**Henrik** How long since you were last in Vienna?

**Konrad** More than forty years. When . . . I left for Singapore.

**Henrik** How do you find it?

**Konrad** Changed. As you'd expect. But I wanted to see it again before I died.

**Henrik** They say at our age, you live until you get tired of living.

**Konrad** I am tired of living. But Vienna: for me it was the tuning fork of the universe. The most beautiful thing in my life. If I was talking to someone and they didn't respond to the word Vienna, I lost interest in them. The stones of Vienna contain everything I ever loved: memories, music; friendship.

*Pause.*

**Henrik** But, as you say, it's changed.

**Konrad** Yes.

**Henrik** At least, here, hardly anything has changed.

**Konrad** No.

*Pause.*

Did you ever travel?

**Henrik** Not unless I had to. I served out my time in the army, you know, just as I'd promised my father I would. Not that there was much satisfaction to be derived. The collapse of the monarchy. The revolution.

**Konrad** Yes, I heard about all that.

**Henrik** You may have heard about it: we were obliged to live through it.

**Konrad** Towards the end of 1917, I was working way up country, deep in the jungle, hundreds of miles away from anywhere. And one day, sharp at noon, four thousand labourers, covered in mud, came out of the swamps and presented me with a whole series of demands. More money. Shorter hours. And so on. I rode down to Singapore, where I discovered there was a revolution going on in Russia. How could they have known? No radio, no telephones. And that's when I understood that if something's really important to you, you don't need a machine to find out about it.

**Henrik** Is that so?

**Konrad** I'm sure it is. When did Krisztina die?

**Henrik** How do you know she's dead?

**Konrad** She's not here, is she? Where else could she be, except in her grave?

**Henrik** She's buried in the grounds. Not far from the greenhouses. She chose the spot herself.

**Konrad** How long ago did she die?

**Henrik** Eight years after you left.

**Konrad** She was only thirty.

**Henrik** That's right.

**Konrad** What did she die of?

**Henrik**  Some quite rare blood condition. I've forgotten the name.

**Konrad**  So: way back in 1907. Were you still in the army?

**Henrik**  Oh, yes; I served all the way through the war.

**Konrad**  What was that like?

**Henrik**  Horrifying. Especially that last winter, up there in the north.

**Konrad**  I often felt I should have come home and rejoined the regiment.

**Henrik**  Many of us felt the same way.

**Konrad**  The thing was, by that time, I was already a British subject. You can't keep changing your nationality every ten years.

**Henrik**  No. In my opinion, you can't change your nationality under any circumstances. We swore an oath to the Emperor, or the King, as my father always insisted on calling him.

**Konrad**  The world we swore to uphold doesn't exist any more.

**Henrik**  It does to me.

**Konrad**  No: there was a world worth living and dying for, but it's vanished now, gone. What's replaced it means nothing to me at all.

**Henrik**  Well, to me it's still alive.

**Konrad**  That's because you're still a soldier.

*It's starting to grow dark; and Henrik rises to his feet, puts his glass down, turns on a couple of switches to generate some discreet background lighting and also lights an oil lamp, which stands on his desk. Then, as the conversation continues, he replenishes their glasses.*

**Henrik** We kept expecting you to come back. Everybody liked you, you know, in spite of your eccentricities.

**Konrad** Eccentricities?

**Henrik** Yes, your worship of music, your artistic nature. We knew it must be hard for you, being a soldier. So your disappearance came as no surprise to us. Even so, we all thought you would be back. Or at least drop us a line. I certainly did, anyway. So did Krisztina.

*Pause.*

But no doubt, with your busy life, you soon forgot us.

**Konrad** No. You never forget the important things. That's to say, I hardly remember anything about the regiment. But you never forget the essentials.

**Henrik** Vienna, you mean; this house.

**Konrad** That's right. The last time I was in this house, for example, Krisztina was alive. Sitting in that chair there.

**Henrik** It was a warm evening, but she was wearing her Indian shawl.

**Konrad** You remember every detail.

**Henrik** I do.

**Konrad** Of course, the details are crucial. They bind everything together. That's what I would dwell on, this detail or that, when I lay in bed listening to that rain drumming against the roof like a machine gun; or when I was with one of those women, with their beautiful, smooth skin and their supple bodies and their enormous, shining eyes; or when I was playing the piano.

**Henrik** Did you sometimes play the Polonaise-Fantaisie?

**Konrad** No, I never played Chopin in the tropics. Too painful.

**Henrik** You remember that evening you played the Polonaise-Fantaisie with my mother?

**Konrad** Yes.

*Henrik looks up at his mother's portrait.*

**Henrik** Of course, she was always wanting to turn Chopin into some kind of honorary Frenchman, but you explained to us how Polish he was; and finally admitted he was related to your mother.

**Konrad** So he was.

**Henrik** Later on, when we were alone, my father said to me that you would never make a soldier.

**Konrad** Did he?

**Henrik** Yes; I was shocked. He said you were a different breed. He didn't mean it unkindly. When you were ten and he first met you in Vienna and shook your hand and said if you were a friend of mine you would always be a friend of his, he made a lifelong commitment to you, which he would never have betrayed. He seldom gave his hand and when he did it was without reservation. Nevertheless, that evening you played the Polonaise-Fantaisie with my mother, he understood you were a different breed. Of course, for that matter, so was my mother.

**Konrad** In what way?

**Henrik** She came from Paris, from a world of gossip and music and embassy balls; and here she was on the far side of the Hungarian plain, in a castle so remote and so quiet you can hear the snow falling. I remember the look of utter bewilderment on her face as she sat in the window watching my father setting off after wolves with his hunting knife. They loved each other; but there was something insurmountable between them.

**Konrad** You told me a story about her bursting into tears in front of the King.

**Henrik** The King came to stay once; they put him in the yellow bedroom. They gave a ball for him, and it was while he was dancing with my mother: he said something or she said something and all of a sudden she was weeping and the King kissed her hand and brought her back to my father.

**Konrad** What was said?

**Henrik** I don't know: she always refused to explain, even to my father.

*Pause.*

I'm glad you came back. Who else could I ever speak to about such matters?

*Silence. He takes a thoughtful sip of his drink.*

We don't have very much longer to live.

**Konrad** Possibly; but what makes you so sure?

**Henrik** The fact that you've come back. And you know it as well as I do. All this time you've been thinking about it. And now you've come back, because you had no choice; and I've been waiting for you, because I had no choice either. We both knew we would meet again and that then life would be all over.

*Konrad looks as if he's about to protest; then he thinks better of it.*

You see, the kind of secret which stands between us has an enormous power; it's like a butcher's knife slicing through the fabric of life, while at the same time giving it a kind of strength and consistency. And it keeps us alive, it provides us with an inescapable purpose.

*Pause.*

So, while you were out in the tropics, keeping yourself busy, I was here, alone in this forest. And solitude hides as many dangers as the jungle. You lead an entirely ordered existence, you have your house, your title, your rank, and your punctiliously organised way of life. You can't run amok, like one of your Malays, you have to be disciplined as a monk and push everything back inside, without any of the beliefs that sustain a real monk. The only thing you can do is wait.

**Konrad** What for?

**Henrik** The moment you are finally able to discuss all the things that forced you into that solitude with the man responsible. And you prepare yourself for that moment for years, ten years or forty years or forty-one years, whatever it is, the way you might prepare yourself for a duel. Practising every day, using your memories as weapons, until they're sharper than sabres. And finally the moment arrives. Am I making any sense?

**Konrad** Yes; I couldn't agree with you more.

**Henrik** Good. I mean, if I hadn't been so sure you would come back one day, I'd have set off myself to find you in your house in London or in the tropics or wherever you might have been. But you're right, you don't need a radio or a telephone to know what's really important: and I knew you'd be back. I waited you out.

**Konrad** I feel I should say that I was well within my rights to go away. It's true I didn't warn you or say goodbye to you, but I knew you'd understand I had no choice. It was the right thing to do.

**Henrik**  You had no choice?

**Konrad**  No.

**Henrik**  Well, now we're getting close to the heart of the matter.

*In the ensuing pause, a gust of wind rattles the windows and in the distance a sulphurous bolt of lightning cuts through the darkness. The electricity fails as a rumble of thunder rolls across the night sky. Henrik calmly sets about lighting a second oil lamp.*

**Henrik**  I'm afraid the electricity supply is still rather fragile in this part of the world.

**Konrad**  I'm used to it: London is subject to blackout every night.

**Henrik**  Is that so?

**Konrad**  There's been fighting in the skies all summer; I believe the Luftwaffe's getting more than it bargained for.

**Henrik**  I don't suppose this can be the most convenient time to travel across Europe.

**Konrad**  No.

**Henrik**  One more indication of how important this meeting must have been to you, wouldn't you say?

**Konrad**  You may be right.

**Henrik**  I believe I am. Is that enough light?

**Konrad**  Ample.

*Henrik resumes his seat, contemplates Konrad for a moment.*

**Henrik**  Now: I often think of that day my father shook hands with you in the alley of chestnuts in the courtyard of the Academy. Possibly because, for some reason, I think of it as the last day of our childhood. But also, no doubt, because, for my father, friendship was just as important as honour. And, to tell you the truth, I think it was even more important for me than it was for him. I hope I'm not making you feel uncomfortable.

**Konrad** Uncomfortable? Not in the least. Please go on.

**Henrik** Do you think there is such a thing as friendship?

**Konrad** Well . . . yes.

**Henrik** I don't mean common interests or professional comradeship. I mean that rare, selfless bond that might just be the most powerful relationship in life. I've sometimes thought there might be something erotic about it, not in the sense of that, in my view, morbid impulse which drives people to seek some kind of satisfaction with those of their own sex, but a kind of eroticism, if this is possible, which has nothing to do with the body. Plato talks about this: about friendship being the noblest feeling that can exist between human beings. It's something you find more reliably among animals. It's a kind of duty. If I'm right, if this is the case, a friend expects nothing in return for his friendship and he entirely accepts all his friend's faults and weaknesses. Consequently, it should make no difference whether his friend is faithful or faithless. I mean, if your friend betrays you and you decide to take revenge, doesn't that imply your friendship wasn't true and genuine in the first place? In other words, we can demand unconditional honour and loyalty from ourselves, but we have no right to expect it in return: and no right to complain if our friend does turn out to be a traitor.

**Konrad** Are you quite certain this hypothetical friend is in fact a traitor?

**Henrik** No. That's why you're here. That's what we're talking about.

*Silence. Henrik settles back in his chair.*

There is such a thing as establishable fact, in the sense of finding out exactly what happened where, when and in what way. But sometimes what actually happened is not the essential thing; it is the *intention* behind what's been done: that's where the true guilt lies. A man can be a murderer and still be quite irreproachable; obviously, everything depends on the motive. We know you ran away. But what was your motive? All these years I've turned it over and over in my mind, weighed up every possible reason: but I'm still no nearer the truth.

**Konrad** 'Ran away' is rather a tendentious expression. I resigned my commission in the regular way, I broke no promises, I left no debts. In what sense did I run away?

**Henrik** Perhaps that's putting it too strongly. But it's certainly what it looked like from my standpoint. You say you left no debts: well, I'm sure you settled your tailor's bill and your wine merchant's – but what about your debt to me? The day you left, it was a Wednesday, I remember, in July, I went, for reasons I'll explain later, to your apartment. Your orderly was there. I asked him to take me up to your living room and leave me there on my own. I'm afraid I conducted a pretty thorough search: you must forgive my curiosity, but I somehow couldn't accept the fact that my closest friend, from whom I had been inseparable for twenty-four years, since childhood, had simply bolted. I thought you might be seriously ill; or momentarily deranged; or caught cheating at cards; or any number of disgraceful crimes, which would however have been less disgraceful than what was beginning to seem overwhelmingly likely: that you had committed some dreadful crime against me. A matter of hours after spending the evening with Krisztina and me, here at the castle, as we had spent so many contented evenings over the years, in friendship and mutual trust, you ran away like a thief in the night. I stood there in your room, which I can still see with absolute clarity; I can smell the English tobacco and see the paintings of horses and the red leather armchair and the divan, which was actually more of a French bed, a double bed. The thing was, it was the first and last time I was ever in your apartment, even though you'd been there for three years before you ran away. I'm sorry, I can see you find that expression disturbing.

**Konrad** Not really: anyway, words are not the issue here, are they?

**Henrik** Aren't they? Is that what you think? Words are not the issue? I thought they were. I always thought they were the only issue.

*Silence. Konrad looks at Henrik, expressionless.*

Anyway, the fact remains, close as we were, that you had never once invited me to your apartment. I always thought it was because you were ashamed of showing it to me because I was a rich man and you were . . . not. Money was the only thing that had ever come between us. You were never quite able to forgive me for being rich.

**Konrad** On the contrary, I was always very well aware that you could hardly be blamed for it.

**Henrik** All the same . . .

**Konrad** You remember that summer you came to stay with my parents in Galicia?

**Henrik** Of course.

**Konrad** We never discussed it, but I knew you understood then what my mother and father had put themselves through on my account.

**Henrik** Yes.

**Konrad** Every time we went out to the Burgtheater and I needed a new pair of gloves, they wouldn't eat meat for a week. Every time I left your servants the correct tip, he would have to go without his cigars for a month. Somewhere in the back end of Poland they had a farm, which I never saw, belonging to my mother; and everything, my uniform, my exam fees, the costs of the duel I fought with that Bavarian, the bouquet I bought for your mother when she passed through Vienna, everything came from there. Eventually, they were forced to sell it. My mother did the marketing herself every day to make sure the cook didn't overcharge her. Do you wonder I nearly killed that Bavarian? It wasn't because I was offended, it was because he was an affront to those two old people in that cramped apartment in that squalid little town. My father adored Vienna, he was born and brought up there, but for the last thirty years of his life, he never set foot in it. No summer holidays, no new clothes, not one stick of new furniture; and all because I was to become the masterpiece they had failed to achieve in their own lives.

**Henrik** Perhaps in some sort of way it made them happy.

**Konrad** I don't know: it certainly weighed me down. I even caught myself wishing them dead sometimes.

**Henrik** Yes.

**Konrad** You mustn't think I envied you going out dancing five times a week, while I stayed in reading and practising the piano and eating scrambled eggs. I may have been jealous about the ballerinas occasionally, but I was quite content to hear about Prince Esterhazy's wine-tasting parties at second hand.

**Henrik** You know nothing would have made me happier than to have provided you with an allowance.

**Konrad** No, but that would have been completely impossible, I know you understood that, even when you saw me counting my socks after they came back from the laundry.

**Henrik** Yes; although at moments like that it was borne in on me that being rich probably was unforgivable. As I rather think you've discovered for yourself by now.

*He rises to his feet.*

Another drink?

**Konrad** Oh; no thank you.

**Henrik** We shall go in to dinner in a moment. I suggest we eat in peace and allow ourselves time to appreciate the wine; and then we can have the conversation you came here to have. Does that seem an acceptable programme?

**Konrad** Entirely.

**Henrik** The carriage is waiting, so of course you can leave whenever you like. Or you're more than welcome to stay the night.

**Konrad** No, I . . .

**Henrik** Well, then, the carriage will take you back to town and tomorrow you can set off back to Vienna or London or Singapore, for all I care. But first I would like you to listen to what I have to say.

**Konrad** Very well.

**Henrik** Your apartment, by the way: as I was saying, I always thought the reason you never invited me there was because you were ashamed of how modest it was. But standing there, the day of your disappearance, I saw that it was exquisite, a real work of art. I couldn't believe my eyes. I remembered you'd once said something about inheriting some little property on the Russian border: and here it was, on the walls, on the floors, translated into crystal and silver and paintings. I realised you were a kind of artist; and how lonely you must have been among us rough soldiers. I was turning all this over in my mind, when I suddenly noticed something: a crystal vase on your piano containing three orchids. Now I knew the only place in this whole region where orchids were grown was in my greenhouses. And I was just pondering the implications of this, when the door opened and Krisztina stepped into the room.

*Silence. Finally, Konrad seems shaken. Henrik, by contrast, turns, light on his feet, his manner entirely casual.*

Shall we go in to dinner?

*Blackout.*

# Three

*A couple of hours later. The wood fire blazes and a number of blue candles have been lit, since the electricity has not yet come back on. Konrad is installed in the brown leather armchair with a cigar and a glass of brandy, while Henrik is more mobile, alternating between the Florentine chair, where he sips at a tiny glass of deep red liqueur, and a restless pacing around the room. Konrad seems calm, but remains tense and watchful, never taking his eyes off Henrik. On one of the occasional tables, someone has placed a blue crystal vase full of dahlias.*

**Henrik** My father was passionate about hunting: he went out every day, whatever the weather; and if it wasn't the season for deer or pheasant, he would be quite content hunting foxes or even crows. My mother detested the whole process. Nothing associated with hunting was allowed in the house; and eventually my father was obliged to have our hunting lodge built, to house his weapons and trophies and accommodate his dogs and falcons. I inherited his enthusiasm, I loved hunting as well; whereas you, of course, were never a huntsman.

**Konrad** I hunted.

**Henrik** Only as a social duty: it was like riding, you had no instinctive feel for it. You always looked rather disdainful and you carried your gun casually, as if it were a walking stick. Anyway: I wanted to speak to you about the hunt we went on, that hot summer's day, the last year of the last century, the day before you ran away. As it happens, it was the last time I ever went hunting in my forest: because something happened on that hunt,

26

something which I only understood in retrospect, your goodbye in fact, something which helped me begin to understand.

**Konrad** Understand what?

**Henrik** It was the most beautiful day. I don't think I've ever loved anything in my whole life as much as the first light of dawn on the day of the hunt. It's dark when you get up, you put on clothes which smell of the forest, wet leaves and air and blood, you eat cold meat and swallow a glass of schnapps, you pick up your gun and inhale the scent of oil and metal. I loved every second of it. The clean taste of the breeze, the bumping of the shooting brake, the leaves slippery underfoot, the birds singing as the light peels back the sky and drops through the trees as if the curtain has just gone up in some enchanted theatre. Actually, at the moment I'm referring to, it was still dark: or to put it more accurately, it was not yet light, it was the precise moment that separates night from day. I was leading, the two of us already far ahead of the gamekeeper and his dog, when suddenly, about three hundred yards away down the forest path, a deer stepped out of the undergrowth. It paused on the path. It couldn't smell us because the wind was blowing towards us; but it tensed and lifted its head and stood there, as if it were somehow paralysed by the inevitable, brought to this exact spot by incalculable but inescapable circumstances.

It's at such a moment you begin to feel that forbidden pleasure experienced at one time or another by all living creatures, perhaps the most intense of all the passions: the urge to be the stronger. It's what the leopard feels as he crouches to spring; or the falcon as it launches into its dive. A man feels it when he has his quarry in his sights. And it's what you felt, Konrad, who knows, possibly for the first time in your life, when you raised your rifle to your shoulder and took aim at me.

*In the ensuing silence, Henrik picks up the decanter and refills Konrad's glass. Konrad looks up at him steadily, exhibiting no trace of alarm. Henrik replaces the decanter and reflects for a moment.*

The truth is, you hated me; you'd hated me for twenty-four years with a passion more or less indistinguishable from love. Passion is not amenable to reason and eventually it has to find some way of expressing itself. Every great passion is hopeless, of course, otherwise it wouldn't be a passion, it would just be a lukewarm inclination or a clever calculation. But you hated me and that made for as strong a bond as if you'd loved me. Now why did you hate me?

*Pause. Konrad shows no inclination to answer.*

As I said, you would never agree to take money from me; and you would never allow our friendship to develop into a genuinely fraternal give and take. I should have taken that as a warning sign: when someone refuses to accept a part of something, it's often because he wants everything. You hated me as a child, from the first moment we met, because there was something in me you wanted and couldn't have. I don't mean you were aware of this at the time: on the contrary, as children, we enjoyed the great gift of a magical friendship: until your character formed and you found you couldn't bear the fact you lacked something I had. What was it? You were a far better student than I was, far more diligent and talented, and, of course, you had your secret feeling for music, your relationship with Chopin. But all along you had some frantic ambition to be something other than what you are; which is the worst and most painful punishment a man can possibly suffer. Life only becomes bearable when you've come to terms with who you are, accepted your own vanity or selfishness or bald head and pot belly, without expecting a pat on the back for acquiring such enlightenment. You have to learn that your desires will never be entirely reciprocated and accept that the people you love will never love you back in quite the way you would hope. You have to accept betrayal; and, hardest of all, you have to accept there are others more intelligent, more admirable and more deserving than you. This is what you couldn't accept. You couldn't accept that for those ten wonderful years in Vienna – and it's so long ago now I can speak of it quite objectively – first at the Academy and then in the regiment, I was so popular and indulged and happy. You thought anybody who was so generally liked must have something whorish about them, that I was so self-assured I actually assumed I must be one of the elect. But if that *is* what you thought you were mistaken: what came to me came because I was so trusting; I genuinely believed the best of everyone, especially you, and that was what everybody responded to, except perhaps you. I thought I was truly blessed.

But of course the world spares nobody. Those who stay modest and humble can have a better run than most, but it won't last for ever. And as youth began to slip away, things started to cool between us. There's nothing sadder, there's no feeling more hopeless, than the cooling of a deep friendship between men. With women, there's always some sense of delicate negotiation; but men have no aim beyond trying to preserve an unwritten pact. I had hoped you might be happy that I moved so easily through the world, just as I admired your bitter intelligence. I thought as I basked in the sunshine of life, you simply chose, of your own free will, to stay in the shadows. Did you share any of these feelings?

**Konrad** I thought you were talking about the hunt.

**Henrik** I was, yes. But all this is connected. After all, if you decide to kill someone, the decision doesn't arrive out of nowhere, you don't just take aim and blast away.

You need to feel you're avenging something unforgivable. How else do you travel from the inseparable bonds of childhood friendship to that forest path? That's what has to be decided before we can go on to talk about the hunt. The moment you point a rifle at someone's head is not the moment of maximum guilt; the guilt, as I've said, is in the intention. And if I say that one day the bonds of friendship between us broke, I need to know if that really is the case; and if it is, I need to know when and why. We were two very different people but *we were friends*!

*He's suddenly spoken very loudly; but without apparently fracturing Konrad's equanimity. Henrik pours himself another liqueur, takes a little time to collect himself.*

We were friends. Not good companions or comrades or fellow-sufferers. What we had was irreplaceable. If we hadn't been friends, you would never have raised your gun against me. And if we hadn't been friends, I wouldn't have gone to the apartment you'd never invited me to. And if you hadn't been my friend, you'd never have run away that day, like a criminal, like a murderer. You'd have stayed and deceived me and undermined me and hurt me, none of which would have been anything like as terrible as what you actually did. Because you were my friend. If you weren't, why would you have come creeping back after forty-one years to the scene of the crime? And here's something surprising and disturbing which has slowly been dawning on me this evening: we're still friends.

You ruined my life. You killed something inside me. And we're still friends. And tonight, I'm going to kill something inside you and then you can go back to London or the tropics or wherever the hell you want to go: and we'll still be friends. Friendship is a very strict obligation: the entire legal systems of great cultures

were founded on its laws. It's stronger than ambition
or self-regard or even sexual desire; and it cannot be
disappointed, because it makes no demands. Even if you
kill your friend, death will not dissolve your friendship.
In fact, as you raised your rifle to kill me, our friendship
was more alive, in that moment, than it had ever been.

I stopped when I saw the deer; and ten paces behind
me, you stopped as well. The deer was listening, not
moving a muscle, somehow sensing danger: yet taking no
evasive action, because somewhere in the heart of mortal
danger lies a kind of attraction. I certainly felt it, when I
heard the cold click of perfectly tempered English steel, as
you released the safety catch. You remember?

**Konrad** Yes. Yes, I do.

**Henrik** And this is when something happened, something
you know as well as I do, but which could never be proved
in a court of law. I felt you move behind me, just as if I'd
been watching you. You raised the gun, tucked it into
your shoulder, closed one eye and took aim: and then I
felt the gun gradually swivel until my head was in the line
of fire. I felt your hand tremble; and all my hunter's
experience told me that from where you were standing, you
could not have been aiming at the deer. You understand,
at that moment, as a hunter, it was the technical aspect
that preoccupied me the most: the angles, the geometrical
disposition of the targets, one of which was me. You took
aim for thirty seconds precisely, I knew that without
looking at a watch. I couldn't move, because I knew my
fate was no longer mine to control: whatever was going
to happen would happen of its own volition. It was a
perfect opportunity: no witnesses, one of those tragic
hunting accidents you read about every year in the
newspapers; but no shot was fired. Suddenly the deer
smelled danger and with a single bound leapt into the
undergrowth. We still didn't move. Then, very slowly,

31

you lowered the rifle. You lowered it with enormous care, in case the air moving round the barrel might whisper to me and betray you; but even so, I knew what you were doing.

What's interesting, of course, is that you still could have killed me, no one would have known the difference, no judge would ever have convicted you; our friendship was legendary, you would have generated nothing but total sympathy. There's no more tragic figure than a man who has accidentally killed his friend. Nobody could have been crazy enough to suggest you'd done it on purpose. You didn't owe me money, you were always treated like a member of the family, everyone knew you were my absolute closest friend.

And yet you didn't pull the trigger. Why? What stopped you? Was it really that the disappearance of the deer robbed you of your objective pretext? Well, it really doesn't matter. What matters is that you wanted to kill me, your hand started to shake, the deer vanished and the moment passed. I didn't turn around. If I had, if I'd looked you in the eye, everything might have been revealed. But I didn't dare. I felt the shame of the victim, the most overwhelming sense of shame you can ever feel. And after a while I just resumed walking down the path; you followed automatically, and I said, without turning, 'You missed your shot.'

You didn't answer. That's when I knew for certain. Any huntsman would have justified himself, said the deer wasn't worth killing, that the shot would have been too risky. But you said nothing. And your silence meant yes, you'd missed the shot that should have killed me. Neither of us said another word. The hunt began; we were separated; and at noon when we stopped for lunch, your beater told me you'd left and gone into town.

*He pauses, noticing that Konrad's cigar has gone out; he picks up a candle to re-light it.*

32

**Konrad** Thank you.

**Henrik** That evening you came to dinner as usual, at seven-thirty. Blue candles on the table. We sat at either end with Krisztina between us. I hadn't seen her that afternoon; apparently she'd gone into town directly after lunch. I found her in the salon shortly before you arrived, sitting in that chair. She was wearing her Indian shawl, even though it was a warm evening. She was reading a book, an English travel book about the tropics; and I suppose she must have been absorbed in it, because she didn't become aware of me until I was right beside her. She looked up at me, startled, and I was shocked by how pale she was. I asked her if she was feeling all right. She didn't answer. She just stared up at me for a long moment, almost as long as the moment I had spent waiting to see if you were going to squeeze the trigger; and the silence was almost as eloquent. She looked into my eyes as if her life depended on finding out what I was thinking, if I was thinking. I think I returned her gaze quite calmly. In the course of the day, I had made the decision never to tell Krisztina or anyone else what had happened at dawn out in the forest. I'd also decided to have a doctor observe you secretly since it seemed to me likely that you were in the grip of some temporary insanity. And I thought the important thing was to maintain dignity, yours in particular, in spite of the fact that if you were not insane, if you'd had some cogent reason to aim your rifle at me, then all three of us had already lost our dignity.

We did discuss the hunt at dinner, but not a word was said about the magnificent deer you'd failed to kill at the beginning of the day; nor did you say anything about leaving the hunt early, which was, to say the least of it, a breach of etiquette. Instead, you asked Krisztina about the book she was reading, you had a long conversation about it, what was it called, what did she think of it, was it interesting – which is curious, because I later discovered it was your book and you had lent it to her. I must say, you both played your roles brilliantly. I remember you asked her if she thought a European could tolerate life in the tropics, if she herself could put up with the rain and the swamps and the jungle, and nothing seemed in the least suspicious. Strange, isn't it, you talked about all that the last time you were here, and now, all these years later, here you are again, still talking about rain and swamps and jungles. Everything goes in circles, I suppose it has to, if it's to be completed. Anyway, you left, as usual, around midnight. And that's my account of the day of the hunt.

Once you'd left, Krisztina went to bed. I picked up the English book and started looking at it. It certainly wasn't her usual kind of thing. I couldn't imagine what interest she might have in the statistics of rubber production in the Malay peninsula. But suddenly I realised the book did have something to say to me: sitting there, holding it, after midnight, when the two people who'd meant most to me in the world had left the room, I understood that it carried a clear, unmistakable message. Krisztina wanted to leave. She wanted to run away from something or someone: and the someone might very well be me.

That was the moment my life split in two: on one side, my childhood, you, my marriage, my happiness; and on the other, the darkness through which I would have to make my way for the rest of my days. I was still very confused. What exactly *had* happened that morning on the hunt? Had I perhaps imagined the whole thing? Had you, my best friend, really wanted to kill me? And if so, why? Of course, the implication must be that there is something between you and Krisztina, but this is such an unlikely notion, I have to rule it out. I know in these situations the third party is always the last to know, but really I would have to have picked up some indication of it along the way. We all have dinner together three or

34

four times a week: and when I'm not with you at the barracks, I'm generally with Krisztina here in the castle. I just have to think about this for a moment and I feel a sense of relief, it's so profoundly implausible. No, there has to be some other explanation. I'm not going to have you watched, like some jealous husband in a farce: all I have to do is talk to you.

I thought about Krisztina for a few minutes and felt even more reassured. Krisztina couldn't be unfaithful, she was incapable of lying, I knew everything there was to know about her. Soon after we married, I gave her a diary bound in yellow velvet, in which we agreed she would write all her most private thoughts and emotions, all the things she felt unable to speak out loud, on condition, and it was her condition, that I could read it whenever I liked or whenever she wanted me to. It was kept in a secret drawer in her dressing room to which she had a key and I had a key. As it happened, it had been some time since I'd last looked at it. So I went upstairs, took out my key and opened the drawer. It was empty.

*Silence. Henrik closes his eyes, as if overcome by a great weariness.*

I thought she was most probably writing in it in her bedroom. I didn't want to disturb her: I thought I'd ask her where it was the next day. You see, the whole thing had been Krisztina's idea in the first place, when we were on our honeymoon in Paris: she said it would be like a perpetual declaration of love. It was only much, much later, long after she was dead, that I realised you only make such careful preparations to confess if you somehow know that one day there will be something that actually has to be confessed. She said she wanted me to have everything: her body, her soul and her innermost thoughts. But she was on honeymoon. She'd gone from a modest house in a small town nursing her sick old musician

35

father, to this castle, a long honeymoon in Paris, London and Rome, a sea voyage, things she could never have dreamed of. Of course she thought she was in love. It was only later that she understood she had only been grateful.

From the beginning, she filled her diary with the most surprising confessions, some of which were disturbingly candid and not at all flattering to me. The thing was, I was happy, I was rich, I was in love, I was thirty years old, I loved my career. No wonder she found me lacking in modesty, rather self-satisfied even: I was. Not that I didn't feel, like everyone who is unreasonably happy, a kind of anxiety at the heart of my happiness, a fear that this couldn't possibly last. But for the moment everything was perfect. Despite the things Krisztina wrote in her diary. 'You are irredeemably vain,' she would say; or she would describe being followed by a man in Algiers who spoke to her in an alley and made her feel for a moment that she wanted to go away with him. But maybe my formula was wrong just now: maybe you confess certain things in order to avoid having to confess what's genuinely fundamental to your life. In any event, I had felt certain that day that you had intended to kill me; I had listened to you discussing the tropics in some detail with Krisztina; and now the diary was gone. And so I decided to travel into town the next day, to go to your apartment and ask you . . .

*He breaks off, sighs and shakes his head as if at his own stupidity.*

Ask you what? I still hadn't understood that whatever I asked you and whatever you may have answered could not in any way alter the facts. Still, the next day, I ordered the carriage and drove into town. I stood in your apartment coming to terms with the fact that you had run away. I stood in that mysterious room full of beautiful objects, trying to understand what had happened and what was happening, when the door opened and Krisztina appeared.

*Konrad leans forward and stubs out his cigar; then he
looks back at Henrik, attentive.*

She saw me and stopped in the doorway. She said: 'Has
he gone?' Her voice was uncharacteristically hoarse.
'Yes,' I said. 'He's gone.' I'd never seen her look so
beautiful. Her eyes were bright and she was so pale, she
looked as if she'd lost a gallon of blood. 'He's run away,'
she said, 'the coward.'

**Konrad** She said that?

*He's spoken involuntarily and Henrik looks at him for
a moment, assessing his slight confusion. Konrad
clears his throat.*

**Henrik** Yes. And that's all she said. I said nothing more
either. We stood in silence for a moment. Then Krisztina
began to look around the room. I watched her. As you
probably know, you can look at things in a room in one
of two ways: as if seeing them for the first time; and as if
seeing them for the last. Krisztina was looking at the room
as if to check that everything was in its place. I had the
sense that if I made one unexpected movement, something
would be done or said that could never be mended . . .
She looked around as if to commit to memory things she
had often seen before: the pictures, the objects, finally the
wide French bed. Then she closed her eyes for a moment;
turned; and left. I watched her walk down the garden
path, between the rose bushes, climb into her trap, pick
up the reins and go.

*The power comes back on; the bulbs flicker and light up.
Henrik does not react; instead he looks penetratingly
at Konrad, who for the first time is plainly hanging on
his every word.*

I hope I'm not tiring you.

**Konrad** No. Not at all. Please go on.

**Henrik** I'm sorry to go into so much detail: but, as you said yourself, the details are crucial. And I don't have very much more to say. You'd run away, Krisztina had ridden off in the trap and I . . . I was standing there, wondering what I could possibly do for the rest of my life. I summoned your orderly and asked him when you had left. On the early express, he said, which meant you'd left for Vienna. Had you taken much luggage? Just a few civilian clothes. What orders had you left? To give up the apartment and sell the furniture. Anything else? Nothing. We looked at each other. He was a boy of no more than twenty . . . and he was looking at me with such pity that quite suddenly I lost control. I grabbed him by the lapels and almost jerked him off his feet. You know it was always best for me never to grab hold of people or things: I generally tended to break them; so I released him and heard his boots smack down on the parquet. There was only one question on the tip of my tongue: the lady who's just left, how many other times has she been here? But I knew if he refused to answer, I might kill him; and if he did answer, I might also kill him, and possibly not only him. And in any case the question was unnecessary, because I knew Krisztina must have been there any number of times.

*He leans back in the chair and his arms drop exhaustedly by his sides. Then he speaks, quietly and tentatively.*

And what's more it was the wrong question. The real question was why all this had happened in the first place; and to what extent the guilt was mine.

*He gets up and moves around the room for a moment, coming to rest by one of the darkened windows.*

One is responsible for one's fate, don't you think? Or rather, something in our character causes us to open a particular door and invite our fate to step in. No one is strong or cunning enough to avoid the disaster provoked by the iron laws of his character. Of course, it was you who introduced me to Krisztina without letting drop the slightest hint you might be interested in her yourself. You used to have your scores copied by her father, after his arthritis had put an end to his concert career . . .

As our honeymoon was coming to an end, we went down to Lake Garda, because Krisztina wanted to pay a visit to the sanatorium where her mother had died. It was surrounded by palm trees, and the light was so delicately hazy, it was like standing in one of our greenhouses. Krisztina walked around these melancholy pale-yellow buildings; and for the first time I sensed that she and I might not be entirely compatible. At the same moment, as if calling from far, far away, I heard my father's sad voice speaking of you, Konrad: saying to me that you were a different breed; and there, in that misty park above Lake Garda, I began to realise that Krisztina might also be a different breed. Perhaps, like my father, I had met a woman I loved profoundly, but at whose side I would always remain alone. I began to understand that the feelings which bound me to Krisztina, to my mother and to you were similar, a hopeless longing for otherness, that fundamental otherness of taste or rhythm or desire that is impossible to acquire, but which the other person can never shed, however close or loving the relationship might be.

Krisztina's essential quality was her absolute independence, which I suppose was both an inheritance and a curse. She was something very rare, a natural aristocrat, self-sufficient, unprejudiced and entirely responsive: to music, to the forest, to intelligence and wit. I've never known anyone else take such pleasure in the world's simplest blessings. Well, you know all of this . . .

I still see her face sometimes.

*He looks up at the blank space on the wallpaper.*

There used to be a painting of her up there; I had it taken down and you won't even find a photograph of her anywhere in the house: but I often see her face when I'm half-asleep or when I walk into a room. And talking about her now, I can see her as clearly as I did that evening, sitting in that chair.

*Silence.*

The fact is, that was the last time I ever had dinner with her. The next day, certain inevitable decisions were taken: you left for the tropics and Krisztina and I never spoke to one another again.

*Silence.*

Music: that was the language you used to communicate with my mother and Krisztina, was it not? A language incomprehensible to my father and to me. I detest music. I hate the way certain people can use it to send uninhibited and very likely immoral messages to one another. It has the power to arouse the deepest emotions in those who are sensitive to it, don't you agree?

**Konrad** I do.

**Henrik** Good. Krisztina's father pointed this out to me. He was the only person I ever spoke to, just once, about you and Krisztina. Very near the end of his life, ten years or more after Krisztina died. When I came back from the war. It turned out he knew everything there was to know about the three of us. We sat there, in that dark room full of musical instruments, he listened to everything I had to say, and then he said: 'What do you have to complain about? You're still alive.' He was right. If you survive, you have no right to make accusations: you're the stronger, you've come out on top, you've won your case. As we have.

Of course, I had also survived the Great War. I made no special effort to do so, men were dying all around me, millions of them, but I somehow knew I would come through, because I had unfinished business. So I came home and waited. Now another war has started, millions are dying all over again, and yet you've been able to make your way through this insane conflagration, in order to settle what needs to be settled between us once and for all. Because human nature demands an answer to whatever may be the defining question of a lifetime. And revenge.

I imagine the whole way of life we were brought up to is finally in the process of being swept away: but still, for some absurd reason, the craving for revenge persists. You look as if you have no idea what I'm talking about. Revenge? Between two old men who are half-dead already? Or against the memory of a woman who died more than thirty years ago? What could be more pointless? Nevertheless, it's what I've been waiting for all this time. My revenge is that you should have made your way here across mine-infested seas and barbarously occupied countries, back to the scene of the crime, to reveal the truth and to answer my questions. To answer to me.

*Long silence. Finally Konrad leans forward slightly.*

**Konrad** Very well. Perhaps you're right. Ask away.

*Henrik sits down and takes a moment to gather his thoughts.*

**Henrik** There are two questions I want you to answer. I expect you think you know what they are. You think I want to ask you whether or not you really did intend to kill me on the hunt that day. And you think the second question must be: were you and Krisztina lovers? But neither of these questions really interests me any more. And anyway I know the answers to them: the answers you gave the day after the hunt when you ran away. I know you wanted to kill me that morning: it's not an accusation, I'm sorry for you, it must be terrible to feel driven to kill the person closest to you in the world. Anyway, you don't deny it, do you?

*Konrad looks at him and says nothing.*

I'm not trying to force a confession out of you; what do you think: you think I want to take you to court for adultery and attempted murder? What a shabby betrayal of our friendship that would be. It may be you'd feel better if you told me whatever there is to tell; but I'm not interested in making you feel better. The truth doesn't sit in a few long-forgotten facts or the physical passions of a long-dead woman. We're old and her body has turned to dust. You think I want to know where, when and how often my wife, the love of my life, betrayed me with my closest friend? You could tell me the whole story, but what would be the point? Everything that once made our hearts burst until we thought we would either die or have to kill someone: it's all less than the dust the wind blows across the graveyard. Poking into the secrets of a body which no longer exists: it would just be humiliating for both of us.

Don't you think the idea of fidelity is appallingly selfish? Do we prove our love by demanding fidelity, if our partner finds it nothing more than a subtle prison, in which it's impossible for her to be happy? And if our love fails to make her happy, what gives us the right to expect fidelity? My answers to these questions now I'm old would be quite different to what they were that day when Krisztina left me alone in your apartment and I looked at that bed where the two of you had betrayed me so ignominiously and so unoriginally.

I came back here and waited for Krisztina. I wanted to kill her and I wanted her to beg my forgiveness. But it got dark and she hadn't arrived: so, rather childishly, I took myself over to the hunting lodge. I went to the hunting lodge twelve miles away and I didn't see her again until eight years later, when she was a corpse. Every evening, I had myself informed of what was going on here in the castle; and I waited, I waited eight years for a message, something, anything. But there was no message and I felt as if I were further away from her than you were, out in the tropics. If Krisztina had sent me a message, any message, I would have done anything she asked. If she'd asked for you, I would have crossed the world to bring you back; if she'd wanted you dead, I'd have killed you; and if she'd wanted a divorce, I'd have given her one. But she asked for nothing. Because she too had a strong personality; and she too had been gravely wounded by those she had loved.

By the way, I learned something new this evening from my nurse, from Nini. I'm sure you remember her: she told me Krisztina had asked for me, when she was on her deathbed. She asked for me, not for you; I don't say this with satisfaction – or without it for that matter – merely for your information. She asked for me. It's not much, but it's something. But as I said, by the time I saw her, she was dead. Still extremely beautiful. Not that it's any of your business.

*Konrad leans forward and buries his face in his hands.*

You know, sitting in the hunting lodge in my self-righteous isolation, I began to pity the two of you. I imagined you wracked with guilt and self-reproach, organising your secret meetings in that small town, wretchedly aware of every move being observed by servants and neighbours. The amount of labour for every fifteen stolen minutes on the pretext of a tennis match or a music lesson. Creeping around in the forest, all that miserable ducking and diving, because what else could you do? You had no

43

money, Krisztina had no money, you couldn't run off with her, you couldn't live with her, you couldn't marry her, any moment you could have been exposed, forced to fight a duel with me. No wonder you finally raised that rifle: but the perfect moment arrived and you failed to act on it.

*He breaks off and inspects his fingernails for a moment. Then he looks up.*

I knew almost everything, you see: but there was one thing that tormented me all those years; and this is the first of my questions. I need an answer, please. The morning of the hunt, did Krisztina know that you intended to kill me?

*Slowly, Konrad raises his face from his hands; he blinks a couple of times, as if to clear his head.*

**Konrad** I . . .

**Henrik** Wait, just a moment, I'm not sure I phrased that correctly, it sounded like an accusation, that's not how I meant it. The reason this idea of a premeditated plan occurred to me is that when Krisztina heard that you had run away, what she said was: 'Coward.' As a matter of fact, that was the last word I heard her utter. Coward. What did she mean? Too much of a coward to run away with her? Or too much of a coward to go on the way you had been? Or, as it later suggested itself to me, too much of a coward to go through with a straightforward plan discussed in advance by the two of you?

This is the question I need to have answered before I die. But it wasn't phrased correctly, that's why I interrupted you. No, more accurately, the question is: what was it that you were too much of a coward to do? It's an insignificant enough question, but I feel that if I fail to discover the answer to it, I know nothing. I'm not interested any more in the details of your relationship;

between any woman and man they're pathetically similar; but this goes to the heart of everything.

There is, in fact, another way, I'm almost sure of it, to find the answer I'm looking for. Long after Krisztina died, I found a box with a few scraps in it: an ivory miniature of her mother, her father's signet ring, an orchid I once gave her, dried and pressed . . . and this.

*Out of his pocket he brings the notebook bound in yellow velvet.*

You see, she's tied a ribbon around it and sealed it with her father's ring. I never broke the seal, because I had no means of knowing whether her confession from beyond the grave was addressed to me or to you. All the same, I assume whatever it contains will be the truth. Krisztina never lied.

*He holds the book out towards Konrad: but Konrad makes no move to accept it. He sits there, motionless and expressionless.*

Shall we read Krisztina's message together? Would you like that?

**Konrad** No.

**Henrik** You don't want to read it? Or you don't dare to read it?

**Konrad** I refuse to answer the question.

**Henrik** I see.

*Henrik reflects for a moment. Then, casually, a trace of satisfaction in his expression, he throws the notebook on to the fire, which has burned low, but which revives to send flames licking around the velvet. The two men watch as the notebook burns. Then Henrik turns to Konrad.*

Now answer my original question: that day in the forest, did Krisztina know you intended to kill me?

**Konrad** I also refuse to answer that question.

*Silence. Then Henrik sits back in his chair.*

**Henrik** Good. Very good.

*Silence. Konrad looks at his watch.*

**Konrad** I think that's probably everything. I expect it's time I went.

**Henrik** The carriage is outside.

*They both rise to their feet. Konrad goes to warm his hands for a moment at the dying fire.*

You'll be going back to London?

**Konrad** Yes.

**Henrik** You're going to stay there?

**Konrad** Yes, for the rest of my life.

**Henrik** You wouldn't care to stay overnight? Visit the grave? Or have a word with Nini? I don't believe you've seen her yet.

**Konrad** No: no, I haven't.

**Henrik** When I was eight, my mother took me to France for the first time, to stay with her mother. I was desperately homesick, everything smelled peculiar, and quite soon after I arrived I went down with a raging fever. I was delirious, but it seems I kept asking for Nini. She had been my wet-nurse, you know, she'd lost her own child, she'd always refused to reveal the identity of the father, and her own father had beaten her and thrown her out of the house. Anyway, my illness became worse and worse and eventually they sent for her: it took her four days to get to Paris, by which time I had been given the last rites. She came straight to me, scooped me out of bed, sat me in her lap and began to rock me in her arms. And I started to get better. She saved my life. For this, as it turns out.

*Silence.*

**Konrad** I won't stay the night, if you don't mind. Please give my best to Nini.

**Henrik** Thank you. I will.

*He begins to escort Konrad towards the door; but Konrad suddenly stops in his tracks.*

**Konrad** Two questions.

**Henrik** What?

**Konrad** You said you had two questions. What was the other one?

**Henrik** The other one? I don't know if I should ask you, since you refused to answer the first question. Krisztina's father's reproach was that I had survived. We both did. You by leaving, I by staying. Since she was worth both of us put together, do you think we were justified? Don't you think we have a responsibility to her beyond the grave? You must know she died because you went away and because I stayed and never went near her, because the two of us were more cowardly and despicable than a woman can bear. We were traitors: we ran away from her. That's what you need to know in London, through all the last hours of your lonely life. I already know it. Surviving a woman you loved enough to consider killing for may not be a capital offence but it's undoubtedly a criminal act. She's dead and we're alive. What did we possibly hope to achieve by surviving her? Wasn't the central truth of your existence that somewhere in the world there was a woman you loved and that she was the wife of a man you also loved? Nothing else counts, does it, but what remains in our hearts?

**Konrad** In our hearts?

**Henrik** So, the second question has to do with the true meaning of our lives. Was the true meaning of our lives not to be found in the pain of longing for a dead woman? I don't know the answer, it's a difficult question. What do you think? Do you believe, as I do, that what gives our life its meaning is a passion that burns in us for ever, no matter what else may happen, war or peace or the decay of empire? And that if we've experienced such a passion, we may not have lived in vain? I'm talking about a passion for one particular person, one single, mysterious other, good or bad, a passion that bears no relation whatsoever to that person's moral qualities or conduct. And this time, if you can manage it, I would like an answer.

**Konrad** I don't understand why you're asking me: when you know very well the answer is yes.

*They look at each other for a moment with complete understanding. Then Henrik reaches for the door handle, opens the door and ushers Konrad out.*

*Blackout.*

# Four

*Five minutes later. Henrik stands at the window. From outside comes the clatter and jingle of the departing carriage, the wheels crunching on the gravel. Nini comes in through the open door.*

**Nini** Are you feeling a little calmer now?

**Henrik** I am, yes.

*He moves over to look up at the empty space on the wall.*

You can hang it back up if you like.

**Nini** I will.

**Henrik** It won't make the slightest difference.

**Nini** No, I know.

**Henrik** You watched me being born in this room, Nini. You've been very patient. I shan't detain you much longer. Good night.

**Nini** Good night.

*She reaches up and traces the sign of the cross on Henrik's forehead. Then she kisses him on one cheek.*

Good night, my darling.

*She turns and leaves the room, closing the door behind her. Henrik stands for a moment, motionless, his head bowed.*

*Slow fade to black.*